The Proper Penguin

The Story of B Polite

Cynthia Grosso

Enjoy the Journey!!
Cindy Grosso

The Proper Penguin
The Story of B Polite
Cynthia Grosso

ISBN# 978-0-9767841-6-6
Book price $14.95

Credits

Cynthia Grosso: Author
James B. Waring: Editor
Kevin Scott Collier: Illustrator
Christi Gifford: Layout and Design

In loving memory of my mother,
Stephanie Louise Grosso,
who taught her children the
"Art of Living"
through her graciousness.

Way down south, farther than you might know
Is a world that is warm, but it's covered in snow
It's a world filled with penguins, some small and some big
Their home is the South Pole and it's where they all live

3

If you wander down south and you simply keep going
And you talk as you walk until the sky starts snowing
You will come to a mountain with a white tippy top
Turn right and then left and take two big hops

4

Lean backward, lean sideways, and jump forward three
And follow the arrow that is drawn on the tree
Watch where you are going, do not step in the hole
And soon you will see the word SOUTH on a pole

SOUTH

5

The penguins live there, a whole group roams inside
They'll wave from the pole lights when they see you arrive
Some call them Southern Polar for their beautiful sites
But the penguins that live there, just call them "the lights"

6

This world is quite toasty despite the cold air
Because of the friendliness and the kindness found there
It's a place that is peaceful both inside and out
Being kind to each other is what life's all about

The penguins get their names from this pole where they live
The pole-lights or polites is the name that it gives
And one polite family, we will visit today
They are rising and shining for a great penguin day

8

Bernardo is the father, known as Papa by others
Beatrice, called mama, is a fine penguin mother
Bellisimo the daughter, known as Bella is she
And Bentley the son, is known only as B

9

On any snowy morning, as they waddle on their way
You will hear them greet others, "Good morning," they'll say
"Good morning, Ms. Polite, and Hello to you too
I am well this fine morning and how about you"

10

Greetings sing out like a sweet morning song
And give you a smile to last the day long
When you're speaking out kindly to start someone's day
It turns right around and comes back your way

If your ears are wide open and your eyes aren't asleep
You will smile as you're hearing the pole penguins speak

"You look lovely this morning," says B to his mother
While Bella sits calmly and smiles at her brother
"How nice that you noticed," mama says to her son,
"You've made me feel happy, now go have some fun"

12

"It's Saturday," says B, "and I'll waddle outdoors
But first I'll remember to finish my chores
I'll make up my bed and take out the trash
And next I'll remember before I can dash

To brush my teeth clean, scrub the dirt all away
That's what penguins do to start out the day"

B leaves with his sister as they waddle on their way
To the playground in town, that's where they will play
Bella talks as she waddles and talks without cause
Without interruption, B waits for her pause

14

Bella talks of her friends, her family and school
As she speaks words of kindness, she makes that her rule
And soon they arrive at the playground that day
With the slide and the swings and their friends there to play

They take turns to slide, being careful of others
B puts Bella first, as a kind older brother
They will share the big ball, while they toss it and run
It's a perfect penguin day to play in the sun

16

"I'm hungry," says B, as he opens the door
"Wipe off your feet," says mom, "I just swept the floor"

18

They'll dine as a family, and a blessing they'll say
While using their good manners and talk of their day
"Thanks, Mom, for dinner," Bella says to her mother,
"May we please be excused, both me and my brother"

20

We will help with the dishes and when we are through
We'll finish our homework, that's what we will do
Off to bed we will go, but before we can sleep
We'll give thanks for our family and the friends we did meet

Good night to all children and please visit some time
Just follow the directions on the southern pole signs
Remember politeness, as all penguins do
And manners will open many doors to walk through

Additional Products from the Charleston School of Protocol and Etiquette

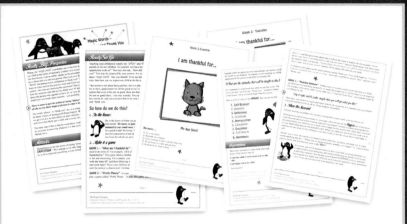

The Proper Penguin - The Story of B Polite

Target age: Infant - 7 years old

12 downloadable lessons teach timeless values from the book.

For more information, please visit:
www.charlestonschoolofprotocol.com/Proper-Penguin

Code of Distinction
Reflecting Your Personal Brand With Excellence

Hardcover, 8 ½" x 5 ½", 108 pages.

Target age: College and Young Professionals

The Code of Distinction challenges the reader to define their personal brand and express it with excellence. The topics include communication excellence, networking excellence, The Million Dollar Meal, Professional and Social Events and Living Your Code of Distinction. For more information, please visit: www.charlestonschoolofprotocol.com/Choose-Civility

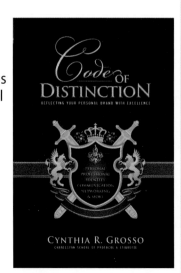

Your Manners Matter
National Civility Program

Three options for purchase:

1. 18 downloadable lessons with audio, and toolkit.
2. 18 downloadable lessons with audio.
3. 9 downloadable lessons with audio.

Target age: Elementary School

Self-directed 9 or 18 lessons cover topics of sportsmanship, introductions, handshake, humility, listening, etc.

Downloadable from website with proper login, password, and a one year subscription. For more information, please visit:
www.charlestonschoolofprotocol.com/childrens-manners-etiquette

Civil Savvy Camp for Children Target age: 9 - 13
A week of camp during the summer with children from all over the world. For more information, please visit: www.charlestonschoolofprotocol.com/childrens-manners-etiquette

Teen Image Workshop Target age: 14 - 18
A week program during the summer with teens from all over the world. For more information, please visit: www.charlestonschoolofprotocol.com/teen-programs